THE ROYAL
GOLDEN JUBILEE
MUSIC COLLECTION

1952 - 2002

THE ROYAL
GOLDEN JUBILEE
MUSIC COLLECTION

1952 - 2002

Wise Publications
London / New York / Paris / Sydney / Copenhagen / Berlin / Madrid / Tokyo

Exclusive Distributors:

Music Sales Limited
8/9 Frith Street, London W1D 3JB, England.

Music Sales Pty Limited
120 Rothschild Avenue, Rosebery, NSW 2018, Australia.

Order No. AM974798
ISBN 0-7119-9543-5
This book © Copyright 2002 by Wise Publications.

Cover photographs by Cecil Beaton, courtesy of Camera Press.
Printed in Great Britain.

Your Guarantee of Quality
As publishers, we strive to produce every book to the highest commercial standards.
This book has been carefully designed to minimise awkward page turns and to make playing from it a real pleasure.
Particular care has been given to specifying acid-free, neutral-sized paper made from pulps
which have not been elemental chlorine bleached.
This pulp is from farmed sustainable forests and was produced with special regard for the environment.
Throughout, the printing and binding have been planned to ensure a sturdy, attractive publication
which should give years of enjoyment.
If your copy fails to meet our high standards, please inform us and we will gladly replace it.

www.musicsales.com

British Grenadiers

Traditional

In march time

Some talk of A - lex - an - der, and some of Her - cu - les; of
Hec - tor and Ly - san - der, and such great names as these; but of
all the world's brave he - roes, there's none that can com - pare with a
tow, row, row, with a tow, row, row, to the Bri - tish Gren - a - dier.

2. Those heroes of antiquity ne'er saw a cannonball,
Or knew the force of powder to slay their foes withal;
But our brave boys do know it, and banish all their fears;
Sing tow, row, row, sing tow, row, row, for the British Grenadiers.

3. Whene'er we are commanded to storm the palisades
Our leaders march with fusees, and we with hand-grenades;
We throw them from the glacis, about the enemies' ears;
Sing tow, row, row, sing tow, row, row, for the British Grenadiers.

4. And when the siege is over, we to the town repair
The townsmen cry, "Hurrah, boys! here comes a Grenadier
Here come the Grenadiers, my boys, who know no doubts or fears!"
Sing tow, row, row, sing tow, row, row, for the British Grenadiers.

5. Then let us fill a bumper and drink a health to those
Who carry caps and pouches, and wear the loupéd clothes;
May they and their commanders live happy all their years
Sing tow, row, row, sing tow, row, row, for the British Grenadiers.

March From Scipio

By George Frideric Handel

Quick march (♩ = 132)

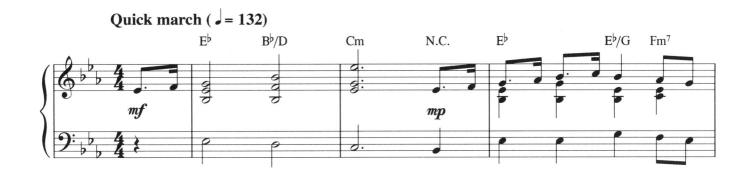

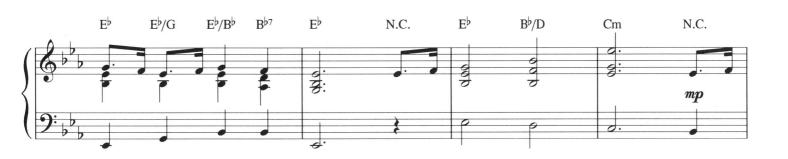

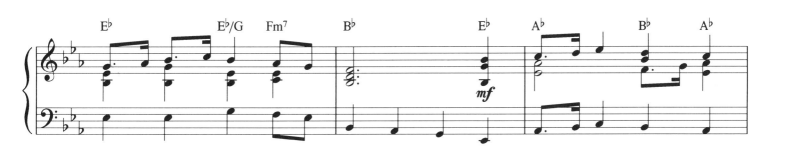

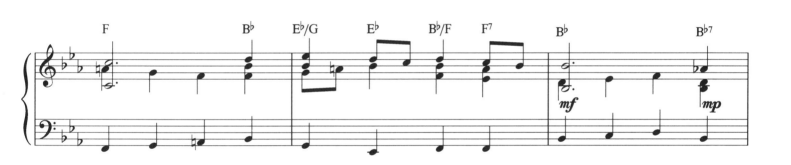

A Tribute To Her Majesty

By Colonel Philip Hills

sov - 'reign of our na - tion state. Loy - al tri - bute to Her

Ma - jes - ty! And___ here's to the Gol - den___ Ju - bi - lee! And___

here's to the Gol - den___ Ju - - - bi - lee!

Here's A Health Unto Her Majesty

Traditional

Zadok The Priest

By George Frideric Handel

Adagio maestoso (♩ = 66)

pp pochiss. a pochiss. cresc.

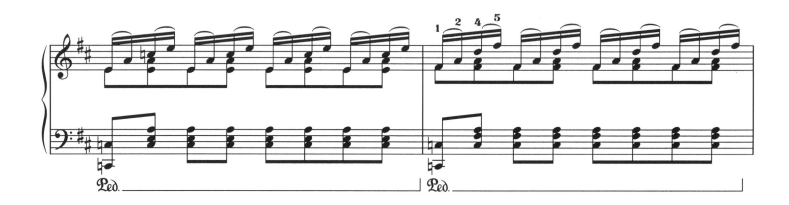

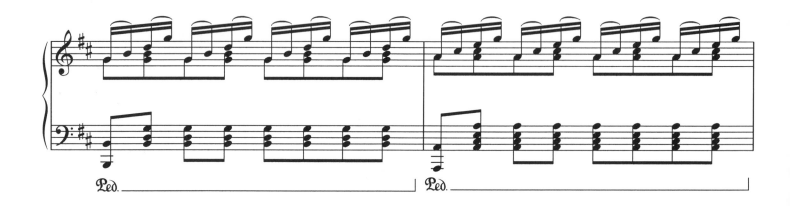

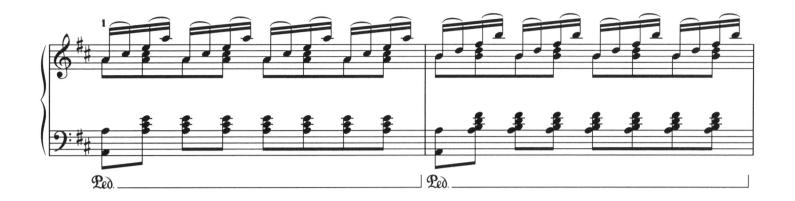

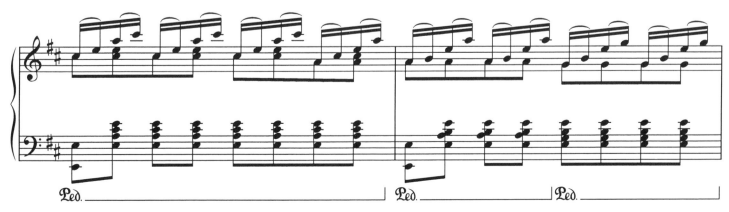

16

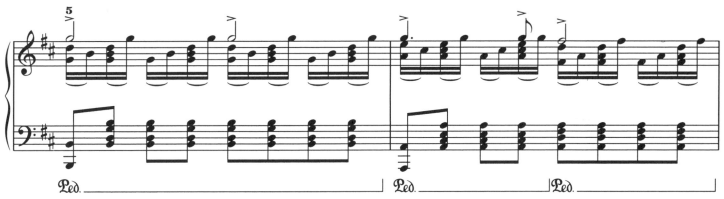

Allegro ($\quarternote$ = 128)

Nimrod
from Variations On An Original Theme 'Enigma' OP. 36
By Sir Edward Elgar

State Occasion

By Robert Farnon

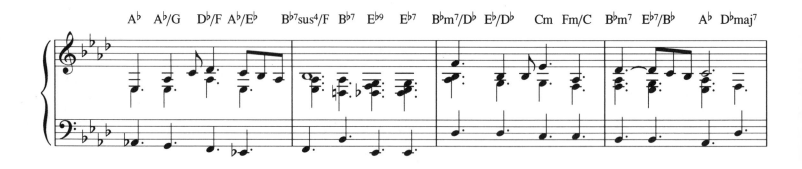

Land Of Hope And Glory

(from 'Pomp And Circumstance, March No. 1')

By Sir Edward Elgar

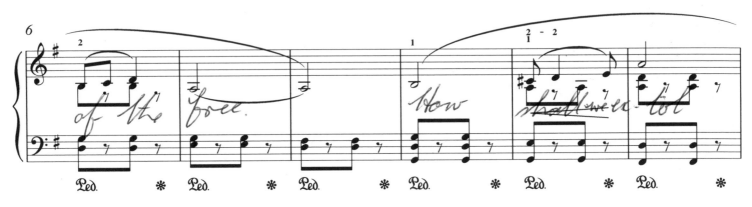

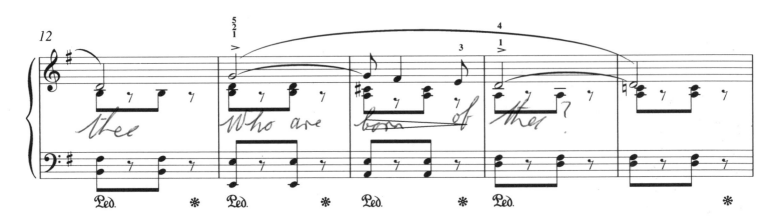

Amazing Grace

Traditional

now I'm found, was blind but now I see. 2. 'Twas home. 4. When we've been there ten thou - sand years, bright shin - ing as the sun. We've

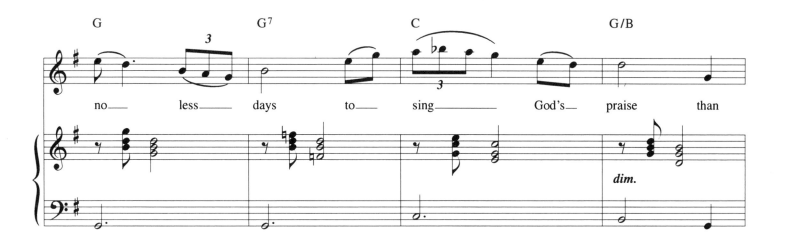

no——— less——— days to——— sing——— God's——— praise than

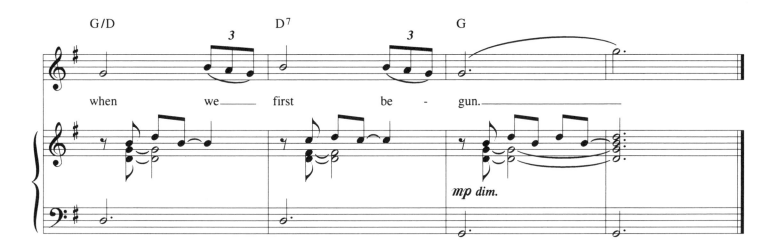

when we——— first be - gun.———

Verse 2:
'Twas grace that taught my heart to fear
And grace my fear relieved
How precious did that grace appear
The hour I first believed.

Verse 3:
Through many dangers, toils and snares
We have already come
'Twas grace that brought us safe thus far
And grace will lead us home.

Suo-Gan

Traditional
Words by Robert Bryan
Arranged by David Seaman

1. Hun - a blent-yn ar fy myn-wes, clyd a chyn-nes yd-yw hon;
(Verses 2 & 3 see block lyrics)

Breich - iau mam-sy'n dyn am dan-at, car - iad mam-sy dan fy mron.

Verse 2:
Huna'n dawel heno, huna
Huna'n fwyn y tlws ei lun
Pam yr wyt yn awr yn gwenu
Gwenu'n dirion yn dy hun?
Ai angylion fry sy'n gwenu
Arnat ti yn gwenunllon?
Tithau'n gwenu'n oldan huno
Huno'n dawel ar fy mron?

Verse 3:
Paid ag ofni dim ond deilen
Gura, gura ar y ddor
Paid ag ofni ton fach unig
Sua, sua ar lan y mor
Huna blentyn, nid oes yma
Ddim i roddi iti fraw
Gwena'n dawel yn fy mynwes
Ar yr engyl gwynion draw.

Irish Tune
From County Derry

Traditional

I Vow To Thee My Country

Music by Gustav Holst
Words by Cecil Spring-Rice

Verse 2:
And there's another country, I've heard of long ago
Most dear to them that love her, most great to them that know
We may not count her armies, we may not see her King
Her fortress is a faithful heart, her pride is suffering
And soul by soul and silently her shining bounds increase
And her ways are ways of gentleness and all her paths are peace.

God Bless The Prince Of Wales

Traditional

Maestoso

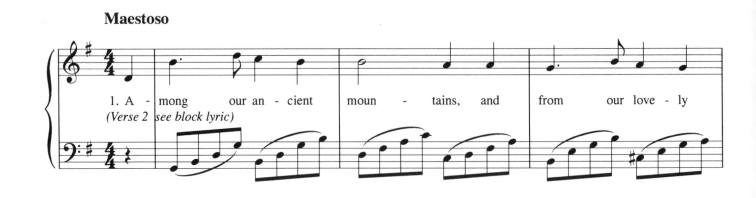

1. A - mong our an - cient moun - tains, and from our love - ly
(Verse 2 see block lyric)

vales, oh, let the pray'r re - e - cho "God

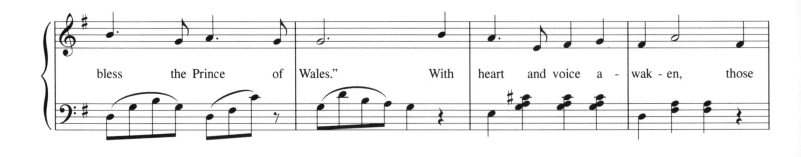

bless the Prince of Wales." With heart and voice a - wak - en, those

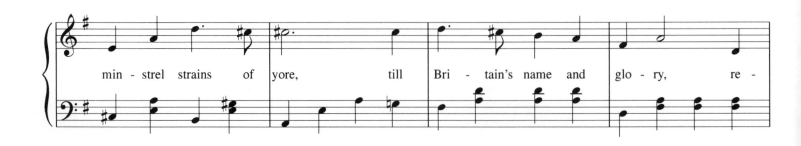

min - strel strains of yore, till Bri - tain's name and glo - ry, re -

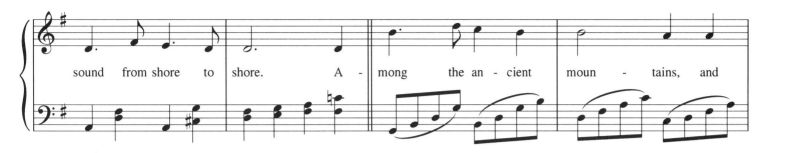

sound   from shore   to   shore.   A - mong   the an - cient   moun - tains,   and

from   our love - ly   vales,   oh   let   the pray'r   re -

-e - cho,   "God   bless   the Prince   of   Wales."

Verse 2:
Should hostile bands or danger
Ere threaten our fair isle
May God's strong arm protect us
May Heav'n still on us smile
Above the throne of England
May fortune's star long shine!
And round it's sacred bulwarks
The olive branches twine.

Among the ancient mountains
And from our lovely vales
Oh let the pray'r re-echo
"God bless the Prince of Wales."

In A Golden Coach
(There's A Heart Of Gold)

Words & Music by Ronald Jamieson

see._____ In a gold - en coach there's a

heart of gold that be - longs to you and

me._____

Rule Britannia

Music by Thomas Arne
Words by James Thomson

Jerusalem

Music by Hubert Parry.
Words by William Blake

The National Anthem

Traditional

hap - py and glo - ri - ous, long to___ reign___

ov - er us; God___ save the Queen!

poco rit.

N.C.

marc.

a tempo

Thy choic - est gifts in store on Her be

54